Slopes

by Michael Dahl

W
FRANKLIN WATTS
NEW YORK • LONDON • SYDNEY

This edition first published in 1998

Franklin Watts
96 Leonard Street
London EC2A 4RH

Franklin Watts Australia
14 Mars Road
Lane Cove
NSW 2066

Original edition published in the United States by Capstone Press
818 North Willow Street, Mankato, Minnesota 56001
Copyright © 1996, 1998 by Capstone Press

ISBN 0 7496 3207 0
Dewey Decimal Classification Number: 621

A CIP catalogue record for this book is available from the British Library.

Printed in Belgium

Photographs: John D. Cunningham 18, FPG/Dennis Cox 8, Image Select/Chris
Fairclough 10, International Stock/Michael Phillip Manheim 14, Andre Jenny 16,
Unicorn/Eric R. Berndt 4, 12, Visuals Unlimited/A. Copley 6, Aneal Vohra cover.

Contents

Words in the text in **bold** type are explained in the Useful words section on page 23.

Machines

Machines are any **tools**
that help people to do work.
A slope
(sometimes called an inclined plane)
can be a machine.
A water slide is an example of a slope.

What is a plane?

A plane is any flat surface.
A sheet of paper, a table top,
the floor, even the street,
are all examples of planes.
The cover of this book is a plane.

What is a slope?

A slope is a plane that has
one end higher than the other.
A playground slide is a slope.
By using a slope you can move
from a high place to a lower one.
Or you can move from a low place
to a higher one.

Making work easier

Slopes help people move heavy objects
from one **height** to another.
Lorries often have fold-out slopes
called ramps to make loading
and unloading them easier.

Moving things faster

Slopes help things to move faster.
The roofs of most houses are slopes.
When it rains the sloping roof
helps the rainwater
to run off quickly.
This stops the rain **pooling**
and leaking into the house.

Steps and ladders

Not all slopes are smooth.
A staircase is a slope.
A ladder is a slope.
These are not smooth,
but they are still tools
because they help
move things up and down.

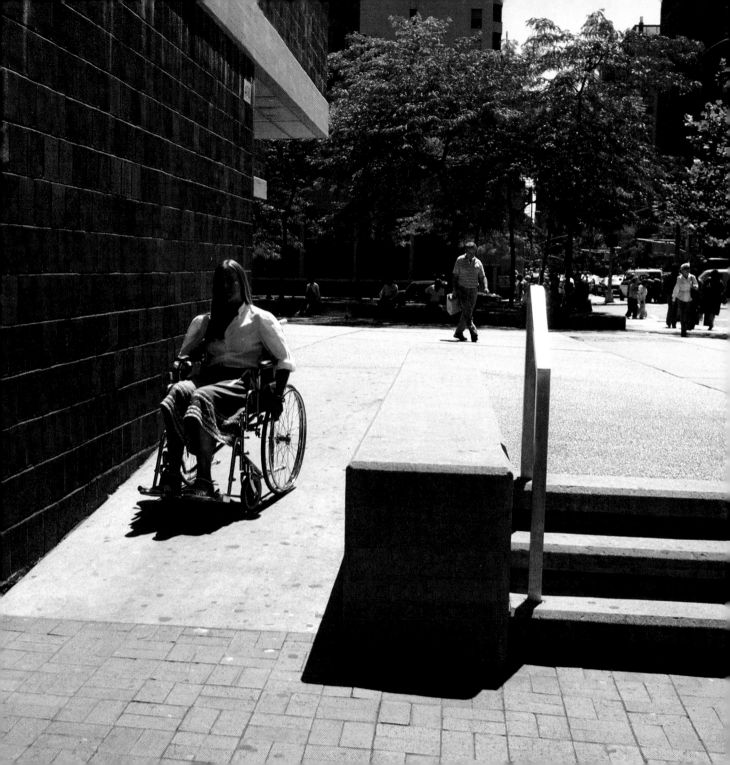

Ramps

A person in a wheelchair
cannot climb stairs or a ladder.
But a wheelchair can move easily
up a smooth ramp.
This is another example of a slope.

Curving ramps

The entry and exit slip-roads
on many motorways are slopes.
The slip-roads curve round in a circle.
In this way they take vehicles
from one level to another.

Wedges

Very small movable slopes
are called **wedges**.
A doorstop is a wedge.
Even a big heavy door will stop
when it runs into a steep little slope
like a doorstop.

Test the power of a slope

Slopes give us an **advantage** when moving heavy objects. This experiment will show you if it is easier to use a long slope or a short one.

What you need

Short board	Shoe box	Short piece of string
Long board	Tin of soup	Thick rubber band

What you do

1   Tie one end of the string around the tin of soup. Tie the other end around the rubber band.
2   Put one end of the short board on the box and the other on the floor.
3   Drag the tin of soup up the slope by pulling on the rubber band. See how much the rubber band stretches.
4   Put the long board on the box.
5   Drag the tin up the second, longer slope. You will see that the rubber band stretches less than before.

It takes less effort to move objects up the longer slope, but it takes more time. The shorter slope takes more effort, but less time.

Useful words

advantage an extra gain that makes something easier to do

height the distance something is above a surface such as the ground

pooling when liquids collect and form a puddle

tool something a person uses to do a job

wedge a special kind of very small slope with a sharp edge at the lowest end

Books to read

Dixon, Malcolm and **Smith, Karen**, *Forces and Movement*, Evans, 1997

Humberstone, Eliot, *Everyday Things*, Usborne, 1991

Turvey, Peter, *The X-Ray Picture Book of Everyday Things*, Watts, 1995

Ward, Alan, *Machines at Work*, Watts, 1993

Index

book 7

doorstop 21

floor 7

heavy objects 11
houses 13

inclined planes 5

ladder 15, 17
loading 11
lorries 11

machines 5
motorways 19

paper 7
planes 7
playground slide 9
pooling 13

rain 13
ramps 11, 17, 19
roofs 13

slide 5, 9
slip-roads 19

stairs 17
staircase 15
street 7

table 7
tools 5, 15

unloading 11

vehicles 19

water slide 5
wedge 21
wheelchair 17

PRINTED IN BELGIUM BY
proost
INTERNATIONAL BOOK PRODUCTION

This
Treasure Cove Story
belongs to

_____

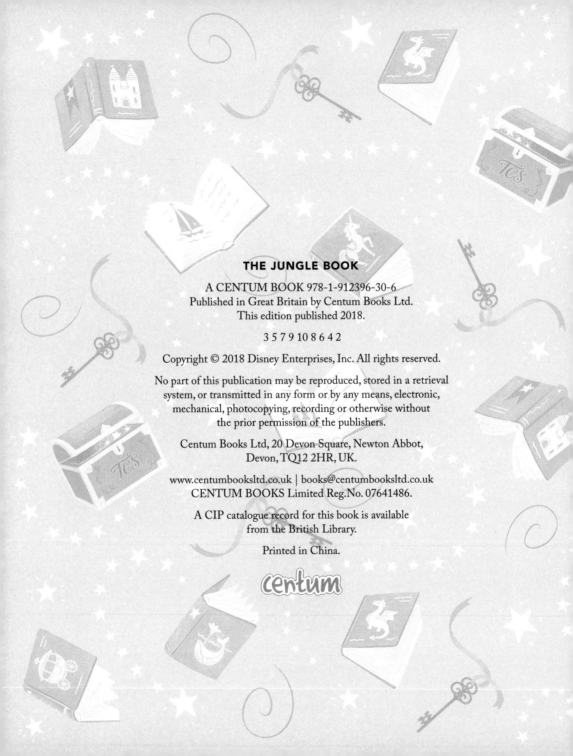

THE JUNGLE BOOK

A CENTUM BOOK 978-1-912396-30-6
Published in Great Britain by Centum Books Ltd.
This edition published 2018.

3 5 7 9 10 8 6 4 2

Centum Books Ltd, 20 Devon Square, Newton Abbot,
Devon, TQ12 2HR, UK.

www.centumbooksltd.co.uk | books@centumbooksltd.co.uk
CENTUM BOOKS Limited Reg.No. 07641486.

A CIP catalogue record for this book is available
from the British Library.

Printed in China.

centum

Walt Disney's

THE JUNGLE BOOK

Many strange legends are told of the jungles of far-off India. They speak of Bagheera the black panther and of Baloo the bear. They tell of Kaa the sly python and of the lord of the jungle, the great tiger Shere Khan. But of all these legends, none is so strange as the story of a small boy named Mowgli.

A child, left all alone
in the jungle, was found
by Bagheera the panther.
Bagheera could not give the
small, helpless Man-cub care
and nourishment, so he took
the boy to the den of a wolf
family with young cubs
of their own.

That is how it happened
that Mowgli, as the
Man-cub came to be
called, was raised among
the wolves.

Mowgli had lived with the wolves for ten years when the wolf pack called a meeting at Council Rock.

'As you know,' said Akela, the leader of the pack, 'Shere Khan the tiger has returned. If he learns that our pack is harbouring a Man-cub, danger will be doubled for all our families. The Man-cub can no longer stay with the pack.'

Out of the shadows stepped Bagheera
the panther.
'Perhaps I can be of help,' said Bagheera.
'I know of a Man-village where he'll be safe.'

So it was arranged, and when the greenish light of the jungle morning slipped through the leaves, Bagheera and Mowgli set out.

All day they walked and when night fell, they slept on a high branch of a giant banyan tree. All this seemed like an adventure to Mowgli. But when he learned that he was to leave the jungle, he was horrified.

'No!' cried Mowgli. 'I want to stay in the jungle. I'm not afraid. I can look out for myself.' He slipped down a length of trailing vine and ran away.

Mowgli soon met a bumbling bear named Baloo.
Baloo played games with Mowgli and taught him
to live a life of ease. There were coconuts to crack,
bananas to peel and sweet, juicy pawpaws to pick from
jungle trees.

Colonel Hathi, the proud old leader
of the elephant herd, tried to train young
Mowgli in military drills as he led his
troop, trumpeting down the jungle trails.
   Mowgli was having such fun
in the jungle!

But the jungle was dangerous.

Sly old Kaa the python would have loved to squeeze Mowgli tight in his coils.

But Shere Khan the tiger was the real danger to Mowgli. That was because Shere Khan, like all tigers, had a hatred of man.

There were other dangers, too.

One day, Baloo and Mowgli were enjoying
a dip in a jungle river. Suddenly, down swooped
the monkey folk. They snatched Mowgli from the
water before Baloo knew what was happening.

They tossed him through the air from hand
to hand and swung away with him through
the trees.

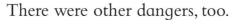

Off in the jungle, Bagheera heard
Mowgli's cry and came with a leap
and a bound.

'The monkeys have carried him off!'
gasped Baloo.

Bagheera and Baloo raced to the
ruined city where the monkeys made
their home. They found Mowgli
a prisoner of the monkey king.

'Teach me the secret of man's red fire,'
the monkey king ordered Mowgli, 'so
I can be like you.'

It took quite a fight for Bagheera
and Baloo to rescue Mowgli!

'Look, Mowgli,' said Baloo. 'I gotta take you to the Man-village.'

But alas, the boy would not listen. He kicked up his heels and ran away again.

This time, his wanderings led him to the high grass, where Shere Khan lay waiting, smiling a hungry smile.

When Mowgli caught sight of the tiger, Shere Khan
asked, 'Well, Man-cub, aren't you going to run?'
But Mowgli did not have the wisdom to be afraid.
'Why should I run?' he asked, staring at Shere Khan
as the tiger gathered himself to pounce.
'You don't scare me.'

'That foolish boy!' growled Bagheera,
who had crept close just in time to hear Mowgli.
   Both Bagheera and Baloo flung themselves
upon the lord of the jungle, to save Mowgli
once more.

They were brave and strong, but the tiger
was mighty of tooth and claw.

There was a flash of lightning and a dead tree
nearby caught fire. Mowgli snatched a burning
branch and tied it to Shere Khan's tail. The tiger,
terrified, ran away. Mowgli was very pleased with
himself as he strutted between the two weary
warriors, Bagheera and Baloo.

A little later, Mowgli
reached the Man-village. From
ahead came a sound he did not
know. He peeked through a bush.
It was the song of a village girl
who had come to fill her water jug.

As he listened to the soft notes of her song, Mowgli felt that he must follow the girl. He crept up the path to the village, drawn by the girl and her song.

Baloo and Bagheera watched the boy's small figure as long as it could be seen. When Mowgli vanished inside the village gate, Bagheera sighed a deep sigh.

'It was bound to happen,' he said. 'Mowgli is where he belongs now.'

Treasure Cove Stories

•Book list may be subject to change.

This
Treasure Cove Story
belongs to

BAMBI FRIENDS OF THE FOREST

A CENTUM BOOK 978-1-912396-29-0
Published in Great Britain by Centum Books Ltd.
This edition published 2018.

3 5 7 9 10 8 6 4 2

Centum Books Ltd, 20 Devon Square, Newton Abbot,
Devon, TQ12 2HR, UK.

www.centumbooksltd.co.uk | books@centumbooksltd.co.uk
CENTUM BOOKS Limited Reg.No. 07641486.

A CIP catalogue record for this book is available
from the British Library.

Printed in China.

centum

A Treasure Cove Story

Walt Disney's Bambi

Friends of the Forest

'Wake up everyone,' chirped the bluebird, one fine autumn morning. 'The Prince is here.'

Bambi's friends watched as the handsome fawn walked gracefully down the path. The possums called out their upside-down greetings and the squirrels and chipmunks chattered hello, too.

'Today, Bambi is going to the lake for the very first time,' Thumper the bunny explained to the old owl. Then he added proudly 'And *I* will introduce him to the animals there.'

The owl looked down at Bambi and said,
'Remember what your mother told you, young
fellow. Be very alert in the forest and run away
quickly if you ever meet with danger.'

Bambi listened carefully as surely his mother
and the wise old owl knew what was best for him.

Not far away, Thumper's sisters had discovered
a small hollow log.

'Would you like to play too, Bambi?' they asked,
as they raced in one end then out the other.

'Oh, I'd like to but I'm too big for that game,'
replied Bambi politely. 'Besides, I'm very busy.'

Then Bambi and Thumper came to the burrow where
their friend Flower lived. They asked the little skunk
if he wanted to join them, but Flower said no.

'There's a very mean fox in the woods,' he warned,
peeking out from behind two big daisies.

Now, Thumper knew he should be afraid, too. But he had so many things to do today, he just didn't have time to worry about a fox.

So off he hopped and Bambi followed close behind as Thumper led the way, deeper and deeper into the big forest.

'Bambi is becoming very brave,' said Mother Quail, as the fawn pranced by, and her family agreed. Bambi had never been so far away from home and never *ever* before had he been away from his mother.

When they finally arrived at the lake, Bambi turned to Thumper. 'It is as beautiful as you said it would be,' he said. And then, sounding a bit disappointed, he asked, 'But where are all the animals?'

Out of the grass came a big, green frog. 'They're here alright,' he told them, 'but they're hiding. That wicked fox was here this morning.'

And then, with a hop and a plop, he disappeared into the water.

The animals were there and they soon came out,
one by one, to meet the handsome Prince.

Mother Duck was the the first to appear. She called
to her ducklings, telling them to come out, too.

Bambi was delighted! He had never before seen birds
who could swim. Nor, for that matter, had he seen birds
who could do such special tricks!

Bambi stepped back, surprised, as the next animal
– a prickly looking fellow – came waddling out from
behind a big rock.

Thumper chuckled. 'Don't worry, Bambi.' he said.
'This is a porcupine. See? He wants to be your friend.'

Next, Bambi met Bernice. He admired her fine, fluffy coat and then, very curious, he asked, 'Why does she wear a mask?'

Thumper chuckled again. 'That's not a mask, Bambi. That's the way a raccoon is *supposed* to look.'

Although the beavers were busy working,
they, too, came over to meet Bambi.

'I've seen your father,' the youngest beaver
told Bambi. 'He comes here often to have a drink.'

Bambi was having a cool, refreshing drink himself, when suddenly he heard a chipmunk's loud nervous chatter.

'Ch-ch-ch-ch-ch-ch-ch! Run and hide the fox is near!'

With a hurry and a scurry, the animals quickly rushed away. But little Thumper, who was so far away from his safe, snug home, didn't dare move. 'Maybe the fox won't notice me,' he thought.

Bambi was frightened, too, but he knew his friend was in worse danger than he was. He saw the large fox slowly and slyly creeping towards the tiny, helpless bunny.

Bambi thought quickly. 'Surely I can outrun the fox!' So, without hesitating, Bambi leapt between the fox and Thumper and, just as Bambi had planned, the fox did start to chase him.

Through the forest they ran, over logs and bushes and rocks and twigs, with the fox never far behind.

Bambi's hooves pounded the ground and his heart beat quickly as the fox got closer and closer.

And then, at the very moment when Bambi felt he could run no more, a large, powerful stag stepped out from behind a tree.

He lowered his majestic antlers and charged. The fox – who was frightened indeed – stopped in his tracks, turned hastily and dashed off into the woods.

Breathless, Bambi looked up at the stag. He knew that
this must be his father, The Mighty King of the Forest,
whom his mother had told him so much about.

The King spoke to his little son. 'You don't know it, Bambi, but you are much too young to outrun such a fox,' he said in a kindly voice. 'But I am very proud of you. The bluebird has told me how you helped your friend.'

That same bluebird also told everyone else what had happened and, by the time the animals arrived at the hill, they saw a very happy Bambi – safe and sound – standing proudly beside his father.

Thumper, who was the happiest of them all, hopped
over to Bambi and looked gratefully up to his friend.

'Thank you for saving my life, Bambi,' he said. 'You're
not only my best friend, but you're my *bravest* friend, too!'

Treasure Cove Stories

*Book list may be subject to change.